Curriculum Motivation Series
A Necessary Dimension in Reading

Leo C. Fay
Professor of Education
Indiana University

Eth Clifford
Children's Author

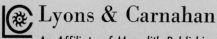 **Lyons & Carnahan**
An Affiliate of Meredith Publishing Company

CHICAGO   WILKES-BARRE   DALLAS   ATLANTA   PASADENA   PORTLAND

Art Director
R. G. Herrington

Illustrations
Carol Burger

Stories

Friends Are Good

Pet on the Roof

Going West

Friends Are Good

Blue Dog

One day, a dog went
to a new house to stay.
He was a big, blue dog.
He was called Blue Dog.

Blue Dog looked out of the house.
He saw some dogs playing.
"I want to play, too," he said.
"I will go play with them."
He ran out to play with the dogs.

"Stop playing!" one dog said.
The dogs all looked at Blue Dog.
Then they laughed at him.

"Look at him!" Red Dog said.
"What a funny dog!"

Blue Dog was surprised.
"Funny?" he asked.
"I am not funny," he said.

All the dogs said, "Yes, you are.
You are funny. We do not like you."

"Why am I funny?" Blue Dog asked.

"You are blue," Yellow Dog said.
"That is why you are funny.
That is why we do not like you.
Dogs are yellow, like me."

"Dogs are red," Red Dog said.

"Dogs are white," White Dog said.

"Dogs are black," Black Dog said.

"Dogs are not blue,"
all the dogs said.
"Go away, Blue Dog.
We will not play with you."

Blue Dog went away.

He was not happy.

Then he saw a kitten.

She was little.

He looked down at Little Kitten.

Little Kitten looked up at him.

"What a funny dog you are!" she said.

She laughed at Blue Dog.

"Why are you laughing at me?"
Blue Dog asked.

"You are blue," Little Kitten said.
"Dogs are not blue.
Kittens are not blue.
It is not good to be blue."

"Why?" asked Blue Dog.

Little Kitten did not know why.
But she laughed at Blue Dog.

Then the dogs saw Little Kitten.
"Look," they said. "A kitten!
Dogs do not like kittens."

"I will run her away!" Red Dog said.

White Dog said,
"I want to run her away, too!"

"We will all run her away,"
the dogs said.
And they all jumped at Little Kitten.

"Help! Help!" Little Kitten said.
She looked at Blue Dog.
"Please help me!"

The dog said, "But I am blue.
Can a blue dog help you?"

"Oh, yes! You can help me!
You are a friend," Little Kitten said.

Blue Dog ran to Little Kitten.

He said, "You are my friend.

I will help you."

Then he said to the dogs, "Go away!"

15

The dogs looked at Blue Dog.
They looked surprised.
"You are a dog," they said.
"Why do you want to help a kitten?"

Blue Dog said, "She is little.
You are big.
The kitten is my friend.
I want to help her."

"But she is a kitten," Red Dog said.
"We do not like kittens."

Blue Dog said, "Yes,
she is a kitten.
But she can not help that.
I am a blue dog. I can not help that.
But a kitten can play with a dog.
We can be good friends."

16

The dogs looked at Blue Dog.

They looked at Little Kitten.

Blue Dog looked big.

That made the dogs run away.

"I laughed at you,"
Little Kitten said.
"But you are good. You helped me.
Now you are my friend.
Now I will not laugh at you."

That made Blue Dog happy.
"Play with me,"
he said to Little Kitten.

"I will play," Little Kitten said.
"Come and play, my good friend."

18

Silly Mouse

Little Kitten was playing
with Blue Dog one day.
She said, "I like to play with you.
We have fun, Blue Dog.
I am happy you came here."

"You are a happy kitten,"
Blue Dog said.
"I will call you Happy."

19

"Good," the kitten said.
"I am not a little kitten now.
I am a big kitten.
I like to be called Happy."

Then Happy said, "I want to eat.
Come to my house.
I will give you some milk."

Blue Dog and Happy went in.

The milk was good.

Blue Dog liked it.

"I WANT SOME MILK, TOO!"

Blue Dog looked around.

He called, "Who said that?"

Happy laughed.

"It is a little mouse," she said.

"He wants something to eat.

Come out, Mouse!"

The little mouse came out.

He looked at Happy.

"I want some milk," he said.

22

"Why do you want milk?"
Happy asked.
"Cats and dogs like milk.
Do you like milk, too?"

Mouse said, "No!
But I want to eat what you eat.
Milk will make me grow big."

Mouse looked at Happy.
"What will you be one day?" he said.

Happy said, "I will be a cat.
Kittens grow big.
Then they are cats."

"I am a big dog now," Blue Dog said.

Mouse said, "I will not be a cat.
And I will not be a dog."

Happy looked at Mouse.
"What are you going to be?" she asked.

"I will be an elephant," Mouse said.

Blue Dog said, "No, friend Mouse!
You can not be an elephant!
A little elephant can grow
to be a big elephant.
But a mouse can not be an elephant."

"Yes, I can," Mouse said.
"I will be a little elephant.
I will eat and eat.
Then I will be a big elephant."

"You are silly!" Happy said.
"You are a little mouse now.
But you will grow to be a big mouse."

Mouse did not like that.
"I can not be an elephant.
Then I will be a lion," he said.
"A lion is big, too.
I will grow to be a big lion."

26

"No, no!" Blue Dog said.
"You can not be a lion.
You can not be an elephant.
But you can be a big mouse."

"Then I do not want milk,"
Mouse said.
"I do not want to grow.
I will not eat.
I will stay a little mouse."

"You are a silly mouse,"
Blue Dog said.
"You can be a big mouse.
And you can be the best mouse."

"Is it good to be the best?"
Mouse asked.
"Is it good to be the best you can be?"

"Yes," Blue Dog said.
"It is good to be the best you can be."

"Then give me something to eat,"
Mouse said.

"Here is some milk," Happy said.
"Now you are not a silly mouse."

28

Dirty Kitten

"Look at Happy!" Mouse said.
"She is a dirty kitten."

"I am not dirty!" Happy said.
"Kittens do not get dirty."

29

Blue Dog said, "Yes, you are dirty.
You played in the street.
Now you have to take a bath."

"No, no!" Happy said.
"I do not want a bath.
Kittens do not take baths."

Mouse looked at Blue Dog.
"Help me give her a bath," he said.
"Dirty kittens take baths.
We will give Happy a bath."

Blue Dog put Happy in a tub.
Mouse put some water in the tub.

Happy did not like water.
She did not like to take baths.
"Take me out!" she called.

"Stop jumping up and down,"
Blue Dog said.
"Mouse has gone to get some soap."

Mouse came with the soap.
He put it in the water.
The soap made bubbles.

Happy did not like soap.
And she did not like bubbles.
Bubbles went around the tub.
Bubbles went around
the three friends.

But Mouse liked bubbles.
He made bubbles and bubbles.

"Stop!" Blue Dog called.
"I can not see Happy now!"

Mouse said, "I will find her."
Then he saw a big bubble.
He jumped on the big bubble.

Mouse had fun.

Mouse and the bubble went up.

They went up and up and up.

Then Mouse looked down.

"Help!" he called.

"I want to come down.

I do not like it up here."

Happy looked up.
She saw Mouse and laughed.
He was going up on a soap bubble!

"Get me down!" Mouse called.
"I will stop making bubbles.
I will not give you a bath."

The bubbles came down.
Mouse came down, too.
Now he was in the water with Happy.

Happy looked at Mouse.
He had bubbles all around him.
"I know what to call you," she said.
"I will call you Bubbles."
Happy jumped out of the water.

Blue Dog helped Mouse
out of the water.
"Yes," he said. "That is good.
Now we will all call you Bubbles."

36

Funny Monkey

Happy saw a ball.
It was in the street.
"I see a ball," Happy said.
"We can play with it, Blue Dog."

Happy and Blue Dog
ran down the street.
They played with the ball.
Then the ball was gone.
They saw it go in a store.

37

Blue Dog and Happy wanted the ball.
They went in the store.
It was a pet store.

"Look at the animals!" Happy said.
"What funny animals!"

Blue Dog looked at the animals, too.
He asked, "Why are they funny?"

The kitten was surprised.
"The animals are not kittens.
They are not dogs.
They do not look like cats and dogs."

39

"No," Blue Dog said.
"They do not look like you.
They do not look like me.
But we are animals.
They are animals.
We are all animals."

One of the animals looked at Happy.
He said, "You look funny!
You are a funny animal."
Then he looked at Blue Dog.
"You look funny, too.
What animals are you?"

"I am a kitten," Happy said.
"And kittens are not funny."

"I am a dog," Blue Dog said.
"Now what animal are you?"

"I am a monkey," the monkey said.

"I can do tricks. Look at me!"

The monkey jumped up and down.

He did monkey tricks.

He looked at Blue Dog and Happy.

"Can you do that?" he asked.

"No," Blue Dog said.

"No," Happy said.

"Monkeys are the best animals.
We can do tricks," the monkey said.
"Dogs can not do tricks.
Cats can not do tricks."

"You are not the best animal,"
Blue Dog said.
"You do monkey tricks.
But you can not do dog tricks.
You can not do tricks I can do."

"And you can not do cat tricks,"
Happy said.
"Look at me do my tricks."
And Happy did her cat tricks.

"Your tricks look funny to me,"
the monkey said.
"But I like you. Yes, I do."

"You do tricks we can not do.
And we do tricks you can not do,"
Happy said.

"Yes," said Blue Dog.
"But we can all be friends."

Pet on the Roof

Dan Wants a Pet

"I wish I had a dog," Dan said.
"I wish I had a cat.
Oh, I wish I had a pet!"

Mother wanted Dan to have a pet.
But the house was too little.
Dan could not have a dog.
He could not have a cat.
He could not have an animal at all.

Dan looked out.

He saw some birds flying.

"Mother! Mother! Come here!

Look at the birds," Dan called.

Mother looked. "Oh, yes," she said.
"They are pigeons."

"Pigeons?" Dan said.
"Why are they flying around here?"

47

"Pigeons stay around here,"
Mother said.
"Mr. Day has pigeons.
They are on the roof.
Do you want to see them?"

"Oh, yes," Dan said.

Mother and Dan went up to the roof.

Mr. Day was on the roof.
The pigeons wanted something to eat.
Mr. Day was feeding the birds.

"Look, Mother, look!" Dan said.
"What is Mr. Day feeding the pigeons?
What do they eat?" he asked.

"I give them corn," Mr. Day said.
"Corn is good for pigeons.
See how fast they eat it?
They like this corn."

"Corn?" Dan asked.

"Yes," Mr. Day said.
"We like corn.
Birds like corn, too."
He looked at Dan.
"Do you want to feed the pigeons?"

"Yes," Dan said.
"I want to feed the birds.
I will give corn to the pigeons."

"Now they want water,"
Mr. Day said.

"See?" Dan asked Mother.
"Look at the pigeons take a bath!"

Mr. Day said,
"Birds like to take baths."

Dan liked the pigeons.

"How funny they are!" he said.

"I wish I could have a pigeon.

A pigeon could be a pet.

It does not stay in the house.

A pigeon could stay on the roof."

Mr. Day looked at Dan.

"I know you want a pet," he said.

"And I will give you a pigeon.

But will your mother let you have one?

Ask her and see."

Dan said, "Oh, Mother!

Please let me have a pigeon!"

Mr. Day said, "Dan wants a bird.
Let him have a pigeon."

Mother looked at Mr. Day.
Then she said,
"I will let Dan have a bird.
But Dan is to help you, Mr. Day.
He is to help you feed the birds.
He is to help you give them water."

She looked at Dan.
"I will! I will!" Dan said.

"Here, Dan," Mr. Day said.
"This one will be your bird.
He is called Homer."

Dan jumped up and down.
"Homer!" he said. "I like that.
Now you are my pigeon, Homer."

53

Homer came to Dan for some corn.

"See, Mother?" Dan said.

"He likes me. Homer likes me."

Dan looked at Mother.
Then he said, "I wished for a pet.
And now I have one.
I have a pet on the roof."

The Homing Pigeon

Dan looked out.

"Father!" he called. "Come look!
The pigeons are flying."

Father looked out.
He saw the pigeons.
"Where is Homer?" he asked.

Dan said, "Homer is in the cage.
I have to go up to the roof.
Mr. Day wants me to let him out."

"Look at the pigeons," Mother said.
"Look how far they have gone!"

"How far can they fly?" Dan asked.

Father said, "They can fly far away."

Dan was not happy now.

He did not want Homer to fly far away.

He ran out fast.

He went up to the roof.

Mr. Day was on the roof.

"I am happy to see you, Dan,"

Mr. Day said.

"All my birds are out.

Now you can let Homer out, too."

"No!" said Dan.
"I want Homer to stay in the cage!"

Mr. Day looked at Dan.
"No, no!" he said. "A bird has to fly."

Mr. Day wanted Homer
out of the cage.
He wanted Homer to fly with
the other birds.
Homer wanted to fly with
the other birds, too.

"No! No! No!" Dan said.
"I will not let Homer out.
He is my bird.
I want him to stay here!
I want him in the cage!"

"But why?" Mr. Day asked.

Dan said, "Homer will fly away.
He will fly far away.
Then he will not come back!"

"Oh!" Mr. Day said. "Now I see!
You are afraid
that Homer will go too far.
You are afraid he will not come back."

Dan said, "Yes.
Homer is my pet.
I am afraid he will not come home."

"Oh, no, Dan," Mr. Day said.
"Homer will come back.
Homer is a homing pigeon."

Dan was surprised.
"What is a homing pigeon?" he asked.

"A homing pigeon comes home.
He always comes home," Mr. Day said.
"That is why
he is called a homing pigeon."

60

Dan asked, "Will Homer always come back to me?"

"Yes, he will," Mr. Day said.
"You give him corn and water.
You are a friend.
He will always come home to you."

Dan said, "Homer, I will let you go."
Dan let Homer out of the cage.

Homer flew around.

Then he flew with the other birds.

But he came back. He flew to Dan.

Then he flew away.

But Homer always came back.

Homer always came back home to Dan.

The New Pigeon

"Wait, Dan! Wait!
Wait for me!" Andy called.
"Where are you going, Dan?
Can I come, too?" Andy asked.

"I am going up to the roof,"
Dan said.
"I have my pigeon up there."

"I wish I had a pigeon!" Andy said.
"Where did you get one?"

"Mr. Day let me have one.
He let me have the best pigeon.
My bird is called Homer," Dan said.

"Can I see your bird?" Andy asked.

"Yes," Dan said.
"You can help me feed him."

They went up to the roof.

Dan let Homer out of the cage.

Homer flew to Dan.

"Here, Homer!

Here, Homer," Andy called.

But Homer did not fly to Andy.

Andy looked at all the pigeons.

Mr. Day saw Andy looking
at the birds.
He saw that Andy wanted a bird, too.

"Andy! Dan!" Mr. Day called.
"See what I have!"
Mr. Day looked down at something.

Andy and Dan looked, too.
"A nest!" Dan said. "A bird's nest!"

Andy said, "There is a bird
in the nest!"

Mr. Day asked, "See the egg?
There is an egg in the nest, too.
One day, the egg will hatch.
The mother bird is waiting now.
She is waiting for the egg to hatch."

"Will a bird come out of the egg?"
Andy asked.

"Yes," Mr. Day said.
"A little bird will come
out of the egg.
Then the egg has hatched.
I will give the new bird to you."

"Good!" Andy said.
"Then I will have a bird, too."

One day, Dan and Andy
went up to the roof.
They looked at the egg.
They wanted the egg to hatch.

"I wish I had my bird," Andy said.

Then Mr. Day saw something.
"The egg is hatching now!" he said.

A bird came out of the egg.
"Look! Look!" Andy called.
"There is the new bird!"

"The bird has hatched!" Dan said.
"What a funny bird!
He does not look like a pigeon."

"All new birds look funny,"
Mr. Day said.
"He does not look like a pigeon now.
But he will."

"Will he look like Homer?
Will he fly?" Andy asked.

Mr. Day laughed.
"He will fly. Wait and see," he said.

70

Andy and Dan waited.

They saw the little pigeon grow.

They saw him fly.

Then he looked like the other birds.

One day, Mr. Day said, "Here, Andy.
You can have your pet now.
What do you want to call him?"

"What can I call him?" Andy asked.
"What can we name him, Dan?
Help me give my pigeon a name."

Dan laughed.
"I know what you can name him.
You can name him Mr. New," he said.

Dan and Andy laughed.
It was a funny name.
But it was a good name for a new bird.

The Pigeon Race

One day, Dan went up to the roof.
Andy was there.
Mr. Day was there, too.

Mr. Day said, "Dan! Andy!
I have a surprise for you."

"What is it?" Dan asked.
"Is Homer in the surprise?"

"Yes," said Mr. Day.
"The surprise has something
to do with Homer.
And the other birds are in it, too.
The pigeons are going to race.
You will like to see Homer race."

Andy jumped up and down.
"Can Mr. New race?" he asked.

74

"No," said Mr. Day.
"Mr. New looks big.
But he is too little to race."

"How can birds race?" Dan asked.

"I am going far away," Mr. Day said.
"I will take the pigeons with me.
Then I will let them go.
They will all race home."

"How do you know they will race?"
Dan asked.

"I know," said Mr. Day.
"They are homing pigeons.
They will all race home.
They will all come flying fast."

"But how will we know
who wins?" Andy asked.

"The first bird home always wins,"
Mr. Day said.
"Wait in the house, Dan and Andy.
You will see them flying home.
Then come up here.
You will see the first bird."

Dan laughed.
"I did not know birds could race.
This is fun," he said.

"Yes," said Andy. "This is fun."

Mr. Day said, "I am going now.
I will take the birds with me.
I will take Homer, too."
And he went away with the pigeons.

All day, Dan and Andy looked
for the pigeons.
Andy asked, "Where are the birds?"
Dan said, "I want them to fly back."

"They will come home," said Father.
"The birds have far to fly."

All day, Andy and Dan waited.
But the birds did not come back.
Then Dan said, "It is growing dark.
Where are the pigeons?
Can they fly in the dark?"

"Oh, yes," Father said.
"They may be flying home now.
Come, Dan. Come, Andy.
We can go up to the roof.
We can wait for the birds there."

"I want to wait on the roof, too.
I want to see Homer," Mother said.

They all went up to the roof.
But they could not see the birds.

Then Dan saw something.
"Look there!" he called.
"I see the pigeons!"

"They are too far away.
I can not see Homer," Mother said.

"Look!" Andy called.
"One bird is flying in front.
One pigeon is flying fast.
What pigeon is it?" he asked.

"I know that one!" Dan said.
"It is Homer! Look at him go!"

"Come on, Homer!" Andy called.

Mother laughed.
"He is out in front.
He will be first. Look!" she said.

It was Homer! He flew to Dan.
Then the other birds came down.
They all came home.

"Homer is the best bird!" Andy said.
"He knows how to win races!"

Homer looked at Dan.

Dan laughed. "Homer likes to race.
And Homer likes to win," he said.

84

Going West

The Wagon Train

Pat had some boxes.
She had three big boxes.
She said, "I will play house."

Bill and Bob saw the boxes.
They wanted to play with them, too.
But they did not want to play house.

"You always play house," Bill said.
"Playing house is no fun."

"I know what we can do," Pat said.
"We can play wagon train."

"How?" asked Bob.

"Here," Pat said. "Here is how.
We can get in the boxes.
We can run in them.
Then we will have a wagon train."

"Wait!" Bill said.
"I will draw something on the boxes.
I will draw something on all of them."

"Draw horses and wagons on them!
Draw horses and wagons," Bob said.

"There!" said Bill.
"See? We have a wagon train now."

Bob said, "Get in the wagons.
Then we can play that we are
going out west."

Pat said, "Good!
I want to go out west, too."

Bill said, "We will all go west.
Bob, get in the first box.
Pat and I can get in the other boxes."

"Wagon train, go!" Bob called.

"Wagon train, go!" Bill and Pat said.

The wagon train began to go.
It went fast.
It went all the way down the street.

Then Bob called, "Stop!"

"Why stop?" asked Pat.

"The horses need water," Bob said.
"We will stop at the river."

"Where is the river?" Pat asked.

"Look there!" Bob said. "See?
There is water in the street.
Children are playing in the water.
They are playing in the river."

"That is a good river," Pat said.
"I will give my horse water.
Then we can play in the river."

"No, no," Bob said. "Not now.
We can not stop now.
We have to get to the fort."

"We have to go on," Bill said.
"We have to go on to the fort."

"Why?" Pat asked.

"There are Indians around,"
Bill said.
"That is why we have to go on."

"Oh!" said Pat. She looked around.
"I see Indians now!" she called.
"Look there! Indians!"

"Where are the Indians?" Bob asked.

"They are playing in the river. Come on!" Pat said. "We have to go! They will see the wagon train!"

"Wagon train, go!" Bob called.

The train went on. It went fast.

Then Pat saw some new boxes.
"Look in front of the candy store!"
she called.
"There is the fort!"

"The fort!" Bob said. "We made it!"

The wagon train went on to the fort.

"We can stop now," Bob said.
"But we will have to go on.
We have far to go."

At the Fort

A man came out of the candy store.
He wanted to take the boxes away.

"Mr. Best! Please!" Bob called.
"We need the boxes!"

Mr. Best looked at the children.
"What have we here?" he asked.

"This is a wagon train," Pat said.
"We have come to the fort.
Your boxes are the fort."

"Oh!" said Mr. Best.
"I did not know I had a fort here."

"We have come far," Bill said.
"We are happy to see your fort."

"I am happy to see your wagon train.
I am happy you came," Mr. Best said.
"But I want you to know something.
There are Indians here!"

"Indians are in the store?
How did they get in?" asked Bill.

"I let them in," Mr. Best said.
"They wanted the boxes."

Some children came out of the store.
They went to the boxes.
"We came here first," they said.
"Mr. Best said we
could have the boxes."

"You may have them," Mr. Best said.
"But first, the boxes are a fort.
And you are Indians."

"We are?" a boy said.
He did not know he was an Indian.
He laughed.
"It is fun to be an Indian," he said.
"Are you Indians, too?" he asked Bob.

Bob said, "We are a wagon train."
Bob looked at the other children.
"Who is the Indian chief?" he asked.

"I am the chief," the boy said.
"We need horses. You have horses.
We would like to ride.
My Indians want horses, too."

"Oh, no," Pat said.
"We want the boxes.
They are a fort. They are not horses.
You can not have the boxes."

The chief said, "We have to hunt.
Indians need horses to hunt.
We need to hunt so we can eat."

"Yes, you do need horses," said Bob.
"We want to be friends with you.
You can have the boxes.
We will help you make horses."

Bob and Bill went to the boxes.

Bill said, "I will draw horses on them."

Bob helped him.

Then the fort was gone.

The boxes were horses now.

The Indians laughed.

The horses looked funny.

"Thank you, friends," said the chief.
"Now we have horses, too."
Then the Indians went away
on their horses.

"Now we can go on," said Bob.
"We can go out west.
And the Indians will be our friends.
We will not be afraid of them now."

Mr. Best said, "Wait! Do not go!
First, I will give you something."
It was some candy.

"This candy is good," Pat said.
"I am happy we came to your store!"

"So am I!" said Bill.
"And so am I!" said Bob.

The Wild Animals

"We have far to go," said Bill.
"And we have work to do."
So the wagon train went on.

Pat asked, "Where are we going?"

"We have to find good land.
There is good land out west," Bob said.

"I know!" Pat said.
"I know where there is good land."

"The park!" Bill said.
"That is where we can find good land.
It is cool there, too."

The wagon train went on.
It went down the street.
It went down other streets.
The park was far away.

Then the children saw the park.
It was cool there.
And the park had big trees.

Bob said, "We can get
out of the boxes now."

The children sat down.
They sat on the grass.

"I like the grass," Pat said.
"Grass is cool."

"I like trees, too," Bill said.
"I will have a house one day.
It will have grass around it.
And there will be trees, too."

"There is good land
out west," Bob said.

Then Pat saw a kitten.
"Bob!" she cried. "I saw a lion!"

A dog ran up to the kitten.

"Look there!" Pat called.
"An elephant ran up to that lion!"

106

"You are so silly!" Bob said.
"There are no lions in the west!
And there are no elephants out there!
There are no wild animals at all."

"Oh, yes, there are!" Pat said.
"There are wild animals in the west!
See? There goes one of them now."

Bob asked, "Where?
There are no wild animals here.
This is a park."

"I see a squirrel," Bill said.
"There are squirrels in this park.
But a squirrel is not a wild animal."

Pat said, "That is not a squirrel.
That is a bear!
And a bear is a wild animal!"

The squirrel looked at her.

He did not know he was a bear.

He did not know he was a wild animal.

He did not run away.

Bill looked at the squirrel.

"Pat calls you a bear," he said.

"So I will call you a bear, too."

108

Then Bob looked at the squirrel.
"Look! This bear wants to eat.
But do not be afraid, Pat.
I will give your bear something.
Then he will be a friend."

Bill saw a nut in the grass.
"This is good for a bear," he said.
"I will feed the bear."

"I will give the bear
a nut, too," Bob said.

The squirrel liked the nuts.

"See?" said Bob. "He wanted to eat.
Go away, bear."

The squirrel looked at Bill.
He looked at Bob. Then he ran away.

110

A pigeon saw Bob give
the squirrel a nut.
The bird flew down.
He wanted to eat, too.
But the pigeon did not want a nut.
So he flew away.

"The wild animals are friends.
They are not afraid now," Pat said.

Then Pat saw something.
"Look!" she said. "A big lake!"

"A lake?" Bill asked. "Where?"
Then he saw the lake, too.
It was a little pool for children.

"Look at the children!" Bob said.
"They are playing in the water."

"Come on," Pat said.
"I want to go in the lake.
The water looks so cool."

The children ran down to the pool.
They played with the other children.

"What fun!" Pat said.
"I like the water. And I like the west!"

"So do I," Bill said.

Then Bob saw the squirrel.
And he saw the pigeon.
"Look!" he said.
"The wild animals like the west, too!"

The Path in the Park

The wagon train was out west.
It did not have to go on.

Bob said, "The land is good, here.
There is a big lake.
And the Indians are friends."

"I like it here," Pat said.
"Do we have to go home now?"

"No, we can not go now," Bob said.
"We have to find out first."

"Oh, yes," said Bill.
"We have to find out."

Pat was surprised.
"Find out what?" she asked.

"Look around," Bob said.
"See that path?
Where does it go? What will we find?
I am going to see.
Do you want to go with me?"

"I will go with you," Bill said.
"I want to find out, too."

"So do I," Pat said.
"I will go with you."

Bob went first.

Then Bill went down the path.

Pat walked back of the boys.

"This is the way
Indians walk," Bob said.
"We will walk like Indians.
This is an Indian path."

Pat looked around.

She did not see Indians.

But she did not like to be in back.

She was a little afraid.

A squirrel ran in front of her.

Pat jumped. "Oh, oh!" she said.

Pat had jumped on a stick.
The stick flew up.
It came down
on the path in front of Pat.
She was afraid to go on.
"Oh, oh! Help me!" she called.

Bill and Bob ran to help her.
Then they saw the stick.

"A snake! A black snake!" Pat said.
"It is a snake!"

"Silly!" Bill said.
"You are always afraid."
He looked at Pat.
Then he looked at the stick.
"That is not a snake, Pat!
It is a big, black stick."

"Yes," laughed Bob.
"That is not a snake at all.
Look! I will pick it up for you."

"I do not want it," Pat said.
"Take it away!"

"Oh, take the stick away.
Pat is afraid," Bill said.

120

"Yes, I am," Pat said.
"Take it away."

"No!" Bob said.
"I do not want Pat to be afraid.
I will not take the stick away.
Here, Pat. You take the stick.
It will make a good walking stick."

"A walking stick?" Pat asked.
"Is it a stick and not a snake?"
She looked at the black stick.

Then Pat laughed.
"Now I can see that it is a stick.
It was silly of me to be afraid.
I will make a walking stick out of it.
I like that!" she said.

Then something jumped on the path.
It jumped in front of Bill.
Now Bill jumped.
"What was that?" he asked.

"It looked like a frog!" Bob said.
"I did not know there were frogs here."

They looked for the frog.

It was a little frog.

But it could jump fast.

It jumped in the grass.

"I was afraid of a snake," Pat said.

"But I am not afraid of a frog."

"Find the frog!" Bob called.
"Look in the grass!"

But Bill could not find the frog.
And Bob could not find it.
The frog jumped too fast.

"This is a good path," Pat said.
"But it is growing dark.
I have to go home now."

"We all have to go home," Bill said.
"But I wish I had that frog.
I would like to take it home with me."

Bob looked down the path.
"We will come back," he said.
"One day, we will all come back."

The vocabulary of this first-grade book in the Curriculum Motivation Series is based on the words common to five of the seven most frequently used primers. Only 52 new words and 25 attack words are introduced. The attack words can be derived independently through the use of initial consonant substitution. For the convenience of the teacher, the review words used from the common primer vocabulary are listed in the teacher's guide.

The readability level of *Blue Dog, and Other Stories* is 1.6.

WORD LIST

New Words	Attack Words	New Words	Attack Words
FRIENDS ARE GOOD		29. dirty	. . .
		30. bath	. . .
		31. tub	. . .
5. friends	. . .	32. soap bubbles	. . .
6. dog	. . .	33. . . .	. . .
7. . . .	. . .	34. . . .	. . .
8. asked	. . .	35. . . .	. . .
9. why	that (at)	36. . . .	. . .
10. . . .	. . .	37. monkey store	. . .
11. . . .	. . .	38. animals	. . .
12. . . .	. . .	39. . . .	. . .
13. . . .	. . .	40. . . .	. . .
14. . . .	. . .	41. tricks	. . .
15. . . .	. . .	42. . . .	. . .
16. . . .	. . .	43. . . .	. . .
17. . . .	. . .	44. . . .	. . .
18. . . .	. . .		
19. silly	mouse (house)	**PET ON THE ROOF**	
20. . . .	. . .		
21. . . .	. . .	45. roof	. . .
22. . . .	. . .	46. wish	could (would)
23. grow	cats (hats)	47. birds pigeons	. . .
24. elephant	. . .	48. . . .	. . .
25. . . .	. . .	49. feeding corn	how (now)
26. lion	. . .		
27. best	. . .		
28. . . .	. . .		

127

New Words	Attack Words	New Words	Attack Words
50. . . .	. . .	88. draw horses	. . .
51. does	. . .	89. . . .	. . .
52. . . .	let (pet)	90. . . .	. . .
53. . . .	. . .	91. river	need (feed)
54. . . .	. . .	92. fort Indians	. . .
55. homing	. . .	93. . . .	. . .
56. far cage	. . .	94. candy	. . .
57. . . .		95. . . .	. . .
58. . . .	other (Mother)	96. . . .	. . .
59. back afraid	. . .	97. . . .	. . .
60. always	. . .	98. chief	boy (toy)
61. . . .		99. hunt	so (no)
62. . . .	flew (new)	100. . . .	. . .
63. wait	there (where)	101. . . .	. . .
64. . . .	. . .	102. . . .	. . .
65. . . .		103. wild	land (and)
66. . . .	nest (best)	104. cool	park (dark)
67. egg hatch	. . .	105. grass	sat (cat)
68. . . .	. . .	106. . . .	. . .
69. . . .	. . .	107. squirrel bear	. . .
70. . . .	. . .	108. . . .	. . .
71. . . .	. . .	109. . . .	nut (but)
72. . . .	name (came)	110. . . .	. . .
73. race	. . .	111. . . .	. . .
74. . . .	. . .	112. . . .	lake (take) pool (cool)
75. . . .	. . .	113. . . .	. . .
76. wins	. . .	114. . . .	. . .
77. first	. . .	115. path	. . .
78. . . .	. . .	116. . . .	. . .
79. . . .	. . .	117. . . .	. . .
80. dark	. . .	118. . . .	. . .
81. . . .	. . .	119. . . .	stick (trick) snake (take)
82. . . .	. . .	120. . . .	pick (trick)
83. . . .	. . .	121. . . .	
84. . . .	. . .	122. . . .	. . .
		123. . . .	frog (dog)
		124. . . .	. . .
		125. . . .	
		126. . . .	. . .

GOING WEST

85. . . .	west (best)		
86. . . .	. . .		
87. . . .	. . .		

128